MOTHER GOOSE RHYMES

hinkler

Published by Hinkler Books Pty Ltd
45–55 Fairchild Street
Heatherton Victoria 3202 Australia
www.hinkler.com.au

Illustrators: Andrew Hopgood, Melissa Webb, Gerad Taylor,
Geoff Cook, Bill Wood, Anton Petrov and Marten Coombe
Prepress: Graphic Print Group
Typesetting: Graphicraft Limited

ISBN: 978 1 7418 5020 8

Printed and bound in China

Contents

Contents

Baa, baa, black sheep

Baa, baa, black sheep,
Have you any wool?
Yes, sir, yes, sir,
Three bags full;
One for the master,
And one for the dame,
And one for the little boy
Who lives down the lane.

Monkeys on the bed

Three little monkeys
Jumping on the bed;
One fell off
And knocked his head.
Momma called the doctor,
The doctor said:
'No more monkeys
Jumping on the bed.'

Six little mice

Six little mice sat down to spin,
Pussy passed by, and she peeped in.
What are you doing, my little men?
Weaving coats for gentlemen.
Shall I come in and cut off your threads?
No, no, Mistress Pussy, you'd bite off our heads!
Oh, no, I won't, I'll help you to spin.
That may be so, but you can't come in!

Mother Goose

Old Mother Goose,
When she wanted to wander,
Would ride through the air
On a very fine gander.

Mother Goose had a house,
'Twas built in a wood,
Where an owl at the door
For a sentinel stood.

She had a son Jack,
A plain-looking lad,
He was not very good,
Nor yet very bad.

She sent him to market,
A live goose he bought:
'See, Mother,' says he,
'I have not been for naught.'

Jack's goose and her gander
Grew very fond;
They'd both eat together,
Or swim in the pond.

Jack found one morning,
As I have been told,
His goose had laid him
An egg of pure gold.

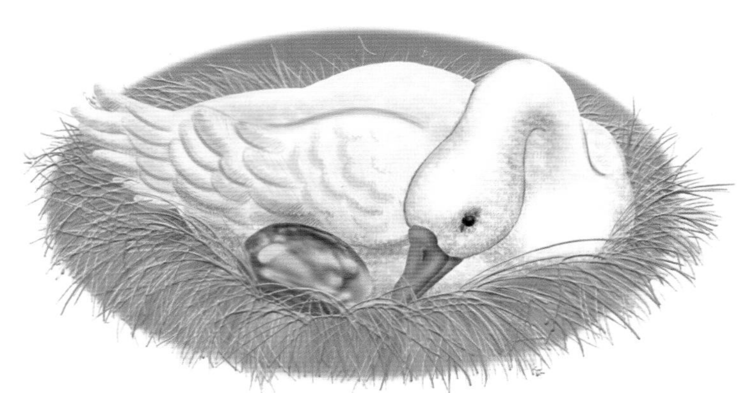

Jack rode to his mother,
The news for to tell.
She called him a good boy,
And said it was well.

Jack sold his gold egg
To a merchant untrue,
Who cheated him out of
A half of his due.

Then Jack went a-courting
A lady so gay,
As fair as the lily,
And sweet as the May.

The merchant and squire
Soon came at his back
And began to belabour
The sides of poor Jack.

Then old Mother Goose
That instant came in,
And turned her son Jack
Into famed Harlequin.

She then, with her wand,
Touched the lady so fine,
And turned her at once
Into sweet Columbine.

The gold egg in the sea
Was thrown away then,
When an odd fish brought her
The egg back again.

The merchant then vowed
The goose he would kill
Resolving at once
His pockets to fill.

Jack's mother came in,
And caught the goose soon,
And mounting its back,
Flew up to the moon.

A wise old owl

A wise old owl lived in an oak,
The more he saw the less he spoke;
The less he spoke the more he heard.
Why aren't we all like that wise old bird?

Pop goes the weasel!

Up and down the City Road,
In and out the Eagle,
That's the way the money goes,
Pop goes the weasel!

Half a pound of tuppenny rice,
Half a pound of treacle,
Mix it up and make it nice,
Pop goes the weasel!

Every night when I go out
The monkey's on the table,
Take a stick and knock it off,
Pop goes the weasel!

Ride a cock-horse

Ride a cock-horse to Banbury Cross,
To see a fine lady upon a white horse;
With rings on her fingers and bells on her toes,
She shall have music wherever she goes.

Fuzzy Wuzzy

Fuzzy Wuzzy was a bear,
A bear was Fuzzy Wuzzy.
When Fuzzy Wuzzy lost his hair
He wasn't fuzzy, was he?

Hey, diddle, diddle

Hey, diddle, diddle, the cat and the fiddle,
The cow jumped over the moon;
The little dog laughed to see such sport,
And the dish ran away with the spoon.

There was a crooked man

There was a crooked man, and he went a crooked mile,
He found a crooked sixpence against a crooked stile:
He bought a crooked cat, which caught a crooked mouse,
And they all lived together in a little crooked house.

Gregory Griggs

Gregory Griggs, Gregory Griggs,
Had twenty-seven different wigs.
He wore them up, he wore them down,
To please the people of the town.
He wore them east, he wore them west,
But he never could tell which he loved best.

Yankee Doodle

Yankee Doodle came to town,
Riding on a pony;
He stuck a feather in his cap
And called it macaroni.

Cobbler, cobbler

Cobbler, cobbler, mend my shoe,
Have it done by half past two.
Half past two is much too late!
Have it done by half past eight.

The house that Jack built

This is the house that Jack built.

This is the malt,
That lay in the house that Jack built.

This is the rat,
That ate the malt,
That lay in the house that Jack built.

This is the cat,
That killed the rat,
That ate the malt,
That lay in the house that Jack built.

This is the dog,
That worried the cat,
That killed the rat,
That ate the malt,
That lay in the house that Jack built.

This is the cow with the crumpled horn,
That tossed the dog,
That worried the cat,
That killed the rat,
That ate the malt,
That lay in the house that Jack built.

This is the maiden all forlorn,
That milked the cow with the crumpled horn,
That tossed the dog,
That worried the cat,
That killed the rat,
That ate the malt,
That lay in the house that Jack built.

This is the man all tattered and torn,
That kissed the maiden all forlorn,
That milked the cow with the crumpled horn,
That tossed the dog,
That worried the cat,
That killed the rat,
That ate the malt,
That lay in the house that Jack built.

This is the priest all shaven and shorn,
That married the man all tattered and torn,
That kissed the maiden all forlorn,
That milked the cow with the crumpled horn,
That tossed the dog,
That worried the cat,
That killed the rat,
That ate the malt,
That lay in the house that Jack built.

This is the cock that crowed in the morn,
That waked the priest all shaven and shorn,
That married the man all tattered and torn,
That kissed the maiden all forlorn,
That milked the cow with the crumpled horn,
That tossed the dog,
That worried the cat,
That killed the rat,
That ate the malt,
That lay in the house that Jack built.

This is the farmer sowing his corn,
That kept the cock that crowed in the morn,
That waked the priest all shaven and shorn,
That married the man all tattered and torn,
That kissed the maiden all forlorn,
That milked the cow with the crumpled horn,
That tossed the dog,
That worried the cat,
That killed the rat,
That ate the malt,
That lay in the house that Jack built.

Simple Simon

Simple Simon met a pieman,
Going to the fair;
Said Simple Simon to the pieman,
'Let me taste your ware.'

Said the pieman to Simple Simon,
'Show me first your penny';
Said Simple Simon to the pieman,
'Indeed, I have not any.'

Simple Simon went a-fishing,
For to catch a whale;
All the water he had got
Was in his mother's pail.

Simple Simon went to look
If plums grew on a thistle;
He pricked his fingers very much,
Which made poor Simon whistle.

He went for water in a sieve
But soon it all fell through;
And now poor Simple Simon
Bids you all adieu.

Peter, Peter, pumpkin eater

Peter, Peter, pumpkin eater,
Had a wife and couldn't keep her;
He put her in a pumpkin shell
And there he kept her very well.

Peter, Peter, pumpkin eater,
Had another and didn't love her;
Peter learned to read and spell,
And then he loved her very well.

Cock a doodle doo

Cock a doodle doo!
My dame has lost her shoe;
My master's lost his fiddling-stick,
And doesn't know what to do.

Cock a doodle doo!
What is my dame to do?
Till master finds his fiddling-stick,
She'll dance without her shoe.

Cock a doodle doo!
My dame has found her shoe,
And master's found his
fiddling-stick,
Sing doodle doodle doo!

Cock a doodle doo!
My dame will dance with you,
While master fiddles his
fiddling-stick,
For dame and doodle doo.

Cock a doodle doo!
Dame has lost her shoe;
Gone to bed and scratched her head
And can't tell what to do.

Jack Sprat

Jack Sprat could eat no fat,
His wife could eat no lean,
And so between them both, you see,
They licked the platter clean.

Pease porridge hot

Pease porridge hot,
Pease porridge cold,
Pease porridge in the pot,
Nine days old.

Some like it hot,
Some like it cold,
Some like it in the pot,
Nine days old.

Betty Botter

Betty Botter bought some butter,
But, she said, the butter's bitter;
If I put it in my batter
It will make my batter bitter,
But a bit of better butter
That would make my batter better.
So she bought a bit of butter
Better than her bitter butter,
And she put it in her batter
And the batter was not bitter.
So 'twas better Betty Botter
Bought a bit of better butter.

Peter Piper

Peter Piper picked a peck of pickled peppers;
A peck of pickled peppers Peter Piper picked;
If Peter Piper picked a peck of pickled peppers,
Where's the peck of pickled peppers Peter Piper picked?

The Gingerbread Man

Smiling girls, rosy boys,
Come and buy my little toys.
Monkeys made of gingerbread
And sugar horses painted red.

Hot cross buns!

Hot cross buns!
Hot cross buns!
One a penny, two a penny,
Hot cross buns!

If you have no daughters,
Give them to your sons.
One a penny, two a penny,
Hot cross buns!

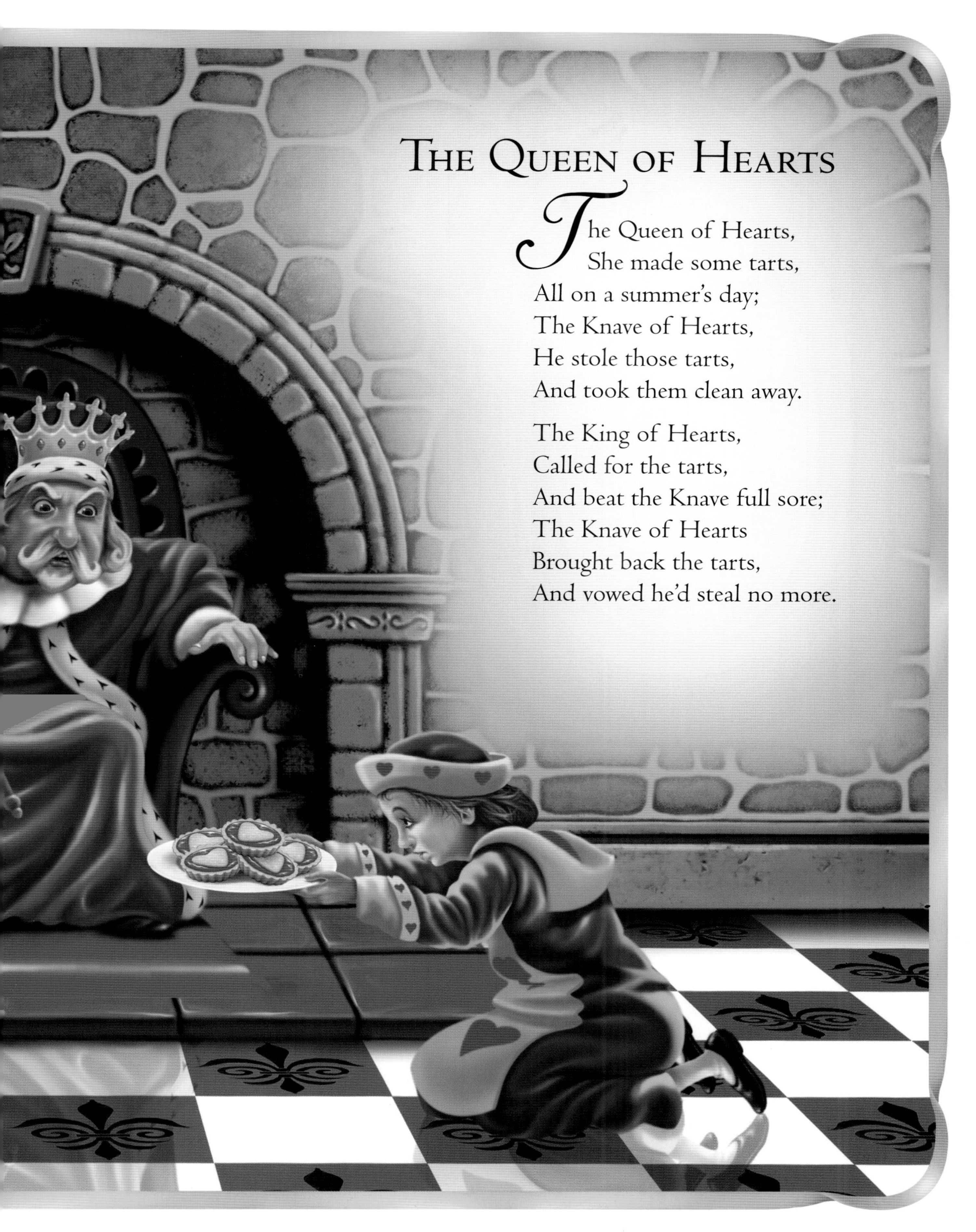

The Queen of Hearts

The Queen of Hearts,
She made some tarts,
All on a summer's day;
The Knave of Hearts,
He stole those tarts,
And took them clean away.

The King of Hearts,
Called for the tarts,
And beat the Knave full sore;
The Knave of Hearts
Brought back the tarts,
And vowed he'd steal no more.

Sleep, baby, sleep

Sleep, baby, sleep,
Thy father guards the sheep,
Thy mother shakes the dreamland tree,
And from it fall sweet dreams for thee.
Sleep, baby, sleep.

Sleep, baby, sleep,
Our cottage vale is deep.
The little lamb is on the green,
With woolly fleece so soft and clean.
Sleep, baby, sleep.

Sleep, baby, sleep,
Down where the woodbines creep.
Be always like the lamb so mild,
A kind and sweet and gentle child.
Sleep, baby, sleep.

Bye, baby bunting

Bye, baby bunting,
Daddy's gone a-hunting,
To fetch a little rabbit skin
To wrap his baby bunting in.

Hush, the waves are rolling in

Hush, the waves are rolling in,
White with foam, white with foam,
Father toils amid the din,
While baby sleeps at home.

Hush, the ship rides in the gale,
Where they roam, where they roam,
Father seeks the roving whale,
While baby sleeps at home.

Hush, the wind sweeps o'er the deep,
All alone, all alone,
Mother now the watch will keep,
Till father's ship comes home.

Come to the window

Come to the window,
My baby, with me,
And look at the stars
That shine on the sea!
There are two little stars
That play at bo-peep
With two little fishes
Far down in the deep.
And two little frogs
Cry, 'Neap, neap, neap,
I see a dear baby
That should be asleep!'

Rock-a-bye, baby, thy cradle is green

Rock-a-bye, baby, thy cradle is green,
Father's a nobleman, Mother's a queen.
And Betty's a lady and wears a gold ring,
And Johnny's a drummer and drums for the king.

She sells sea-shells on the sea shore

She sells sea-shells on the sea shore,
The shells that she sells are sea-shells, I'm sure.
So if she sells sea-shells on the sea shore,
I'm sure that the shells are sea-shore shells.

Rain, rain, go away

Rain, rain, go away,
Come again another day.
Little Johnny wants to play.

It's raining, it's pouring

It's raining, it's pouring,
The old man is snoring;
He went to bed and bumped his head
And couldn't get up in the morning.

I'M GLAD THE SKY IS PAINTED BLUE

I'm glad the sky is painted blue,
And the earth is painted green;
With such a lot of nice fresh air
All sandwiched in between.

Do your ears hang low?

Do your ears hang low?
Do they wobble to and fro?
Can you tie them in a knot?
Can you tie them in a bow?
Can you throw them over your shoulder,
Like a regimental soldier?
Do your ears hang low?

Little Betty Blue

Little Betty Blue
Lost her holiday shoe.
What can little Betty do?
Give her another
To match the other,
And then she may walk in two.

Jack and Jill

Jack and Jill went up the hill
To fetch a pail of water;
Jack fell down and broke his crown,
And Jill came tumbling after.

Then up Jack got and home did trot
As fast as he could caper;
He went to bed to mend his head
With vinegar and brown paper.

TWEEDLEDUM AND TWEEDLEDEE

Tweedledum and Tweedledee
Agreed to fight a battle,
For Tweedledum said Tweedledee
Had spoilt his nice new rattle.
Just then flew by a monstrous crow
As big as a tar barrel,
Which frightened both the heroes so,
They quite forgot their quarrel.

See a pin

See a pin and pick it up,
All the day you'll have good luck;
See a pin and let it lay,
Bad luck you'll have all the day!

Go to bed, Tom

Go to bed, Tom,
Go to bed, Tom,
Tired or not, Tom,
Go to bed, Tom.

See-saw

See-saw, Margery Daw,
Jacky shall have a new master;
He shall have but a penny a day,
Because he can't work any faster.

Pat-a-cake

Pat-a-cake, pat-a-cake, baker's man,
Bake me a cake as fast as you can;
Pat it and prick it and mark it with B,
Put it in the oven for Baby and me.

Two little dicky birds

Two little dicky birds
Sitting on a wall;
One named Peter,
One named Paul.

Fly away, Peter!
Fly away, Paul!

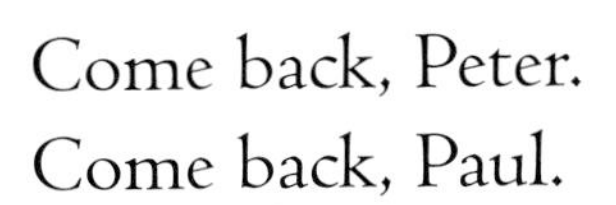

Come back, Peter.
Come back, Paul.

TWINKLE, TWINKLE, LITTLE STAR

Twinkle, twinkle, little star,
How I wonder what you are!
Up above the world so high,
Like a diamond in the sky.

When the blazing sun is gone,
When he nothing shines upon,
Then you show your little light,
Twinkle, twinkle all the night.

Then the traveller in the dark,
Thanks you for your tiny spark,
He could not see which way to go,
If you did not twinkle so.

In the dark blue sky you keep,
And often through my curtains peep,
Do you never shut your eye
Till the sun is in the sky.

As your bright and tiny spark
Lights the traveller in the dark,
Though I know not what you are,
Twinkle, twinkle little star.

Here is the church

Here is the church,
And here's the steeple,
Open the doors,
And see all the people.

I'M A LITTLE TEAPOT

I'm a little teapot, short and stout,
Here is my handle, here is my spout.
When I see the teacups, then I shout,
'Tip me over and pour me out.'

Teddy Bear, teddy bear

Teddy bear, teddy bear,
Turn around.

Teddy bear, teddy bear,
Touch the ground.

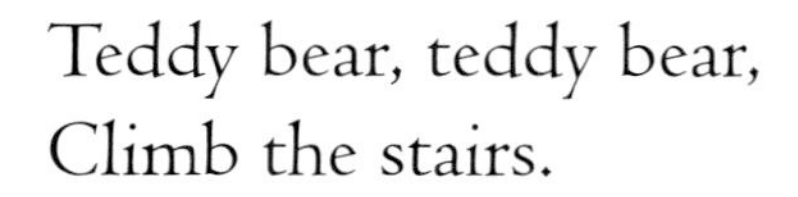

Teddy bear, teddy bear,
Climb the stairs.

Teddy bear, teddy bear,
Say your prayers.

Teddy bear, teddy bear,
Turn out the light.

Teddy bear, teddy bear,
Say goodnight.

Oh where, oh where, has my little dog gone?

Oh where, oh where,
Has my little dog gone?
Oh where, oh where can he be?

With his ears cut short
And his tail cut long,
Oh where, oh where is he?

Ding dong bell

Ding dong bell,
Pussy's in the well.
Who put her in?
Little Johnny Green.
Who pulled her out?
Little Tommy Stout.
What a naughty boy was that,
To try to drown poor pussy cat,
Who never did him any harm,
But killed the mice in his father's barn.

Three little kittens

Three little kittens, they lost their mittens,
And they began to cry;
Oh, mother dear, we sadly fear
That we have lost our mittens.
What! Lost your mittens, you naughty kittens!
Then you shall have no pie.
Mee-ow, mee-ow, mee-ow,
No, you shall have no pie.

Three little kittens, they found their mittens,
And they began to cry;
Oh, mother dear, see here, see here,
For we have found our mittens.
Put on your mittens, you silly kittens,
And you shall have some pie.
Purr-r, purr-r, purr-r,
Oh, let us have some pie.

Three little kittens put on their mittens,
And soon ate up the pie;
Oh, mother dear, we greatly fear
That we have soiled our mittens.
What! Soiled your mittens, you naughty kittens!
Then they began to sigh,
Mee-ow, mee-ow, mee-ow,
Then they began to sigh.

The three little kittens, they washed their mittens,
And hung them out to dry;
Oh, mother dear, do you not hear
That we have washed our mittens?
What! Washed your mittens, you good little kittens,
But I smell a rat close by.
Mee-ow, mee-ow, mee-ow,
We smell a rat close by.

Ladybird, Ladybird

Ladybird, ladybird, fly away home,
Your house is on fire, your children are gone;
All but one, and her name is Ann,
And she crept under the pudding pan.

LITTLE MISS MUFFET

Little Miss Muffet
Sat on a tuffet,
Eating her curds and whey;
Along came a spider,
Who sat down beside her
And frightened
Miss Muffet away.

Old woman, old woman

Old woman, old woman,
Shall we go a-shearing?
Speak a little louder, sir,
I'm very thick of hearing.
Old woman, old woman,
Shall I love you dearly?
Thank you very kindly, sir,
Now I hear you clearly.

A TISKET, A TASKET

A tisket, a tasket,
A green and yellow basket.
I wrote a letter to my love,
But on the way I dropped it.
I dropped it, I dropped it,
And on the way, I dropped it.
A little boy picked it up,
And put it in his pocket.

The Owl and the Pussycat

The Owl and the Pussycat went to sea
In a beautiful pea-green boat;
They took some honey, and plenty of money
Wrapped up in a five-pound note.
The Owl looked up to the stars above,
And sang to a small guitar,
'O lovely Pussy, O Pussy, my love,
What a beautiful Pussy you are,
You are, you are!
What a beautiful pussy you are!'

Pussy said to the Owl, 'You elegant fowl,
How charmingly sweet you sing!
O, let us be married; too long have we tarried:
But what shall we do for a ring?'
They sailed away, for a year and a day,
To the land where the bong-tree grows,
And there in a wood a Piggy-wig stood,
With a ring at the end of his nose,
His nose, his nose,
With a ring at the end of his nose.

'Dear Pig, are you willing to sell for one shilling
Your ring?' Said the Piggy, 'I will.'
So they took it away, and were married next day
By the turkey who lives on the hill.
They dined on mince and slices of quince,
Which they ate with a runcible spoon;
And hand in hand, on the edge of the sand,
They danced by the light of the moon,
The moon, the moon,
They danced by the light of the moon.

Edward Lear

Three elephants

One elephant went out to play
Upon a spider's web one day.
He thought it such a tremendous stunt
That he called for another little elephant.

Two elephants went out to play
Upon a spider's web one day.
They thought it such a tremendous stunt
That they called for another little elephant.

Three elephants went out to play
Upon a spider's web one day.
The web went creak,
the web went crack
And all of a sudden,
they all ran back.

Five little ducks

Five little ducks went out one day
Over the hills and far away.
Mother duck said, 'Quack quack, quack quack!'
But only four little ducks came back.

Four little ducks went out one day
Over the hills and far away.
Mother duck said, 'Quack quack, quack quack!'
But only three little ducks came back.

Three little ducks went out one day
Over the hills and far away.
Mother duck said, 'Quack quack, quack quack!'
But only two little ducks came back.

Two little ducks went out one day
Over the hills and far away.
Mother duck said, 'Quack quack, quack quack!'
But only one little duck came back.

One little duck went out one day
Over the hills and far away.
Mother duck said, 'Quack quack, quack quack!'
But none of those five little ducks came back.

Mother duck she went out one day
Over the hills and far away.
Mother duck said, 'Quack quack, quack quack!'
And all of those five little ducks came back.

The animals went in two by two

The animals went in two by two,
Hurrah! Hurrah!
The animals went in two by two,
Hurrah! Hurrah!
The animals went in two by two,
The elephant and the kangaroo.
And they all went into the ark
For to get out of the rain.

The animals went in three by three
Hurrah! Hurrah!
The animals went in three by three,
Hurrah! Hurrah!
The animals went in three by three,
The wasp, the ant and the bumblebee.
And they all went into the ark
For to get out of the rain.

The animals went in four by four,
Hurrah! Hurrah!
The animals went in four by four,
Hurrah! Hurrah!
The animals went in four by four,
The great hippopotamus stuck in the door.
And they all went into the ark
For to get out of the rain.

The animals went in five by five,
Hurrah! Hurrah!
The animals went in five by five,
Hurrah! Hurrah!
The animals went in five by five,
They felt so happy to be alive.
And they all went into the ark
For to get out of the rain.

The animals went in six by six,
Hurrah! Hurrah!
The animals went in six by six,
Hurrah! Hurrah!
The animals went in six by six,
They turned out the monkey
because of his tricks.
And they all went into the ark
For to get out of the rain.

The animals went in seven by seven,
Hurrah! Hurrah!
The animals went in seven by seven,
Hurrah! Hurrah!
The animals went in seven by seven,
The little pig thought he was going
to heaven.
And they all went into the ark
For to get out of the rain.

The animals went in eight by eight,
Hurrah! Hurrah!
The animals went in eight by eight,
Hurrah! Hurrah!
The animals went in eight by eight,
The slithery snake slid under the gate.
And they all went into the ark
For to get out of the rain.

The animals went in nine by nine,
Hurrah! Hurrah!
The animals went in nine by nine,
Hurrah! Hurrah!
The animals went in nine by nine,
The rhino stood on the porcupine.
And they all went into the ark
For to get out of the rain.

The animals went in ten by ten,
Hurrah! Hurrah!
The animals went in ten by ten,
Hurrah! Hurrah!
The animals went in ten by ten,
And Noah said, 'Let's start again!'
And they all went into the ark
For to get out of the rain.

Three jellyfish

Three jellyfish, three jellyfish,
Three jellyfish, sitting on a rock.
One fell off! ... Ooooh ... Splash!

Two jellyfish, two jellyfish,
Two jellyfish, sitting on a rock.
One fell off! ... Ooooh ... Splash!

One jellyfish, one jellyfish,
One jellyfish, sitting on a rock.
One fell off! ... Ooooh ... Splash!

No jellyfish, no jellyfish,
No jellyfish, sitting on a rock.
One jumped up! ... Hooray!

One jellyfish, one jellyfish,
One jellyfish, sitting on a rock.
One jumped up! … Hooray!

Two jellyfish, two jellyfish,
Two jellyfish, sitting on a rock.
One jumped up! … Hooray!

Three jellyfish, three jellyfish,
Three jellyfish, sitting on a rock.
One fell off! … Ooooh … Splash!

I saw three ships

I saw three ships come sailing by,
Come sailing by, come sailing by,
I saw three ships come sailing by,
On Christmas Day in the morning.

And what do you think was in them then,
Was in them then, was in them then?
And what do you think was in them then,
On Christmas Day in the morning?

Three pretty girls were in them then,
Were in them then, were in them then,
Three pretty girls were in them then,
On Christmas Day in the morning.

One could whistle, and one could sing,
And one could play on the violin;
So joy there was at my wedding,
On Christmas Day in the morning.

Rub-a-dub dub

Rub-a-dub dub,
Three men in a tub,
And who do you think they be?
The butcher, the baker,
The candlestick-maker,
Turn them out, knaves all three.

Little girl, little girl

Little girl, little girl, where have you been?
Gathering roses to give to the queen.
Little girl, little girl, what gave she you?
She gave me a diamond as big as my shoe.

A SAILOR WENT TO SEA, SEA, SEA

A sailor went to sea, sea, sea,
To see what he could see, see, see;
But all that he could see, see, see,
Was the bottom of the deep blue sea, sea, sea!

London Bridge

London Bridge is falling down,
Falling down, falling down.
London Bridge is falling down,
My fair lady.

Build it up with sticks and stones,
Sticks and stones, sticks and stones,
Build it up with sticks and stones,
My fair lady.

Sticks and stones will wear away,
Wear away, wear away,
Sticks and stones will wear away,
My fair lady.

Build it up with iron and steel,
Iron and steel, iron and steel,
Build it up with iron and steel,
My fair lady.

Iron and steel will bend and bow,
Bend and bow, bend and bow,
Iron and steel will bend and bow,
My fair lady.

Build it up with bricks and clay,
Bricks and clay, bricks and clay,
Build it up with bricks and clay,
My fair lady.

Bricks and clay will wash away,
Wash away, wash away,
Bricks and clay will wash away,
My fair lady.

Build it up with silver and gold,
Silver and gold, silver and gold,
Build it up with silver and gold,
My fair lady.

Silver and gold will be stole away,
Stole away, stole away,
Silver and gold will be stole away,
My fair lady.

London Bridge is falling down,
Falling down, falling down.
London Bridge is falling down,
My fair lady.

Goodnight

Goodnight,
Sweet repose,
Half the bed
And all the clothes.

Come, let's to bed

'Come, let's to bed,'
Says Sleepy-head.
'Tarry awhile,' says Slow.
'Put on the pan,'
Says Greedy Nan,
'Let's sup before we go.'

Brahms' Lullaby

Lullaby and goodnight,
With roses bestride,
With lilies bedecked,
'Neath baby's sweet bed.

May thou sleep, may thou rest,
May thy slumber be blest.
May thou sleep, may thou rest,
May thy slumber be blest.

Lullaby and goodnight,
Thy mother's delight.
Bright angels around,
My darling, shall guard.

They will guide thee from harm,
Thou art safe in my arms.
They will guide thee from harm,
Thou art safe in my arms.

Johannes Brahms